© Day One Publications 201
First printed 2007
ISBN 978-1-84625-389-8

Printed 2013

British Library Cataloguing Publication Data available
Published by Day One Publications
Ryelands Road, Leominster, HR6 8NZ
UK 01568 613 740 FAX 01568 611 473
USA 888-329-6630
email-sales@dayone.co.uk
web site-www.dayone.co.uk
North American-e-mail-sales@dayonebookstore.com
North American web site-www.dayonebookstore.com

Designed by Rob Jones
Printed by T J International

What is a church?

1 What do you think a church is?

(Tick the right answer)

☐   A building   ☐   A place of worship

☐   God's house   ☐   A group of Christians who meet together to worship God

HEBREWS 8:10

JOHN 10:14-15

1 CORINTHIANS 1:2

EPHESIANS 5:30

2 What is the Bible's meaning of the word 'church'?

The word 'church' in the New Testament is a translation of the word ecclesia (in New Testament Greek) which means: 'called out'—'assembly'.

How do these words help us to understand what a church is?

A church is a local group of Christians. It is a group of people who know and love the Lord Jesus as their Saviour and Lord. They meet regularly to worship God, serve God, help other people, and tell others about the good news of Jesus Christ.

Some people talk about the universal church. You can't see this church! This means all Christians who have ever been alive, are alive now and will be alive in the future.

What is a church?

3   The early church

The church, as we know it, began on the Day of Pentecost just after Jesus had returned to heaven. The Apostle Peter preached and about 3,000 people became Christians and joined the church.

Check it out in *ACTS 2:38-41.*

ACTS 2:38-47 tells us the kinds of things that the early Christians did as they got together to worship God and learn more about him and serve him.

How did they become Christians? Read *ACTS 2:38-41*.

4   What did the early church do?

When they met together, what do you think they talked about? The weather? Their health? Read *ACTS 2:42, 46-47*.

How did they show their love for God and one another? Read *ACTS 2:44-46*.

What else did they do? *ACTS 13:2-5*

ACTS 11:28-30

1 THESSALONIANS 4:9-10

ROMANS 16:3-5

Where did the early church often meet? Read *ROMANS 16:5*.

What about your church?

1 Evangelical?

If your church is an independent evangelical church, there are hundreds of other churches like it all over the world.

The word 'evangelical' comes from a New Testament Greek word that means good news.

'Evangelical' means a belief in the Bible and a belief in the gospel as explained in the Bible.

Evangelicals accept the Bible as the Word of God and its authority on all matters of faith and practice. An evangelical church will therefore make sure that all it teaches and all it does is based on the truth of God's Word, the Bible. 'Independent' means that a church does not belong to a larger group of churches which decides what that church should do. However, some independent churches have connections with other churches through church fellowship groups like, in the UK, the FIEC (Fellowship of Independent Evangelical Churches) or Affinity.

'Evangelistic' means sharing or spreading the good news.

2 What does your church believe? Many churches have a Basis of Faith which explains briefly or in a summary form what that church believes.

Have a look at your church's Basis of Faith and write in your own words what your church believes about:

God

> Our God is the one only living god Pure Spirit, invisible, with out boddy parts and passion

The Bible

> The bibble is the scripture of all knolledge faith and obeidience and works againt satan

What about your church?

The human race

Salvation

The Lord Jesus Christ

The Holy Spirit

What about your church?

The church

Baptism and the Lord's Supper

The future

3 What does your church do?

Remember what we found out in Chapter 1 about what the early Christian church did in the days of the book of Acts? What can you remember?

The teaching of the Apostles in the New Testament sets out some principles for what Bible-centred churches have done through the centuries and still do today. Let's find out what your church does.

How does your church fit the pattern?

Look at the chart below to find out how your church fits the pattern for churches in the New Testament

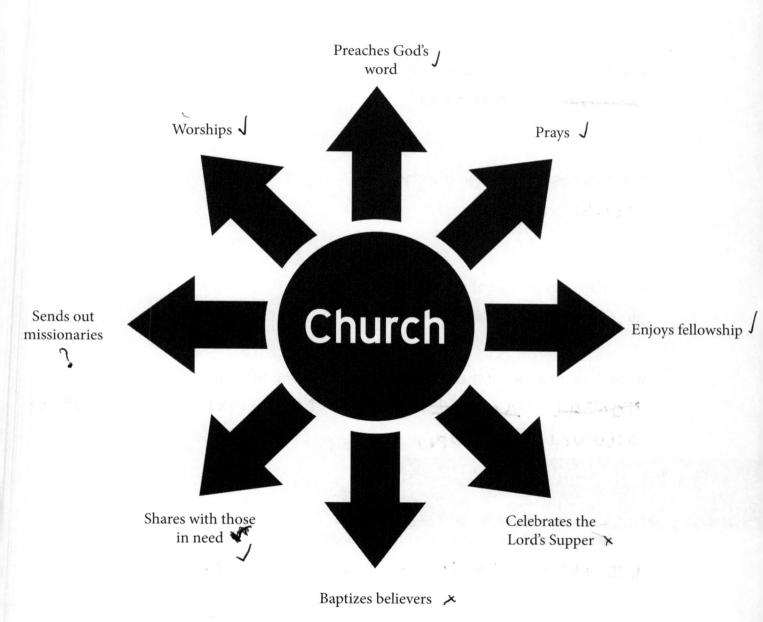

Preaches God's word ✓

Worships ✓

Prays ✓

Sends out missionaries ?

Church

Enjoys fellowship ✓

Shares with those in need ✓

Celebrates the Lord's Supper ✗

Baptizes believers ✗

Whose church is it anyway?

1 Think about your school.

Who is in charge of the school?

> The Head teacher

Who helps to look after the school building?

> ~~No one~~ care taker

Who teaches and helps in the classroom?

> teacher

Who else is in charge of the school?

> Deputyies

What would happen if these people were not doing their jobs?

> ~~TOATAL ANIALATION~~ the school would not be allowed to open

2 Now think about the church.

Who do you think is in charge of the church?

> I think it is a team effort

3 What does the Bible say?

Read *EPHESIANS 5:23B* for the answer.

> The husband is the head of the wife as Christ is the head of the church

Whose church is it anyway?

4 The New Testament gives instructions and examples of how a church should be run for Jesus.

Read the following verses and write down the kinds of people who help to run a church.

EPHESIANS 4:11

1 TIMOTHY 5:17

1 TIMOTHY 4:14

PHILIPPIANS 1:1

5 Are there any special qualifications for church leaders?

YES, not just anyone can serve God in this way.

Read *1 TIMOTHY 3:1-15* and *TITUS 1:5-9* and fill in the job description for an elder.

1 TIMOTHY 5:17 tells us that some elders are preachers and teachers. We call those elders 'pastors'.

Whose church is it anyway?

(continued) Are there any special qualifications for church leaders?

Job description for Pastor/Elder at Any town Church. The following qualifications are essential:

Christian experience

Teaching experience

Family life

Reputation

Personal qualities

5 (continued) Are there any special qualifications for church leaders?

Attitude to money

Attitude to other people

Honesty

6 What are church leaders supposed to do?

Read the following verses to find out:

1 TIMOTHY 5:17

1 TIMOTHY 3:5

EPHESIANS 4:11-14

ACTS 6:1-4

Whose church is it anyway?

7 Deacons

Read *1 TIMOTHY 3:8-12*

It looks like the elders of the first churches needed help. The people who helped them were called 'deacons'.
The word 'deacon' means servant-and Jesus used the same word to talk about himself in *MATTHEW 20:28.*

We should think of all Christians as being 'deacons' as all Christians should be serving God.

In these verses in *PHILIPPIANS 1:1*, it looks like churches had 'deacons' as well as elders in each church. Today some churches think a bit differently about deacons.

What do the verses tell us about someone who is a deacon?

Find out if your church has deacons, and what they do.

8 Why are some church leaders paid to work full-time for the church and not others?

Read *1 TIMOTHY 5:17-18*.

Whose church is it anyway?

9 Church leaders: watch out!

What does: **JAMES 3:1** say?

10 Who are the leaders in your church?

Pastors

Elders

11 Sometimes a church is able to employ people who are not church leaders to work for it.

Does your church do this?

And, if so, what jobs do these people do?

12 What about youth workers, welcome teams, and house group leaders?

Are they paid to work for the church?

What is worship?

1 Sundays

On Sundays the Christian church all over the world meets together for worship and teaching. This is what your church does too, as God has set apart this day.
Read **GENESIS 4:3-5**.
How did the first family worship God?

2 People have been worshippers ever since the beginning of the world.

Read **EXODUS 20:1-6**.
Whom does God want people to worship?

What are your ideas about this?

What do these verses teach us about worship?

DEUTERONOMY 6:13

PSALM 8:2-4

PSALM 19:1

JOHN 4:23-24

What is worship?

3 Worship of God in Old Testament times was different from worship in New Testament times.

Worship in Old Testament times helped to prepare God's people for the coming of the Messiah, the Rescuer. All the details of the place of worship (for example, the Temple) and the ways of worship (for example, the sacrifices) taught about God and about the Messiah.

Where did God's people go to worship God in Old Testament times?
EXODUS 26: 1

1 KINGS 8:12-13

Where did God's people worship him when Jesus was on earth?
LUKE 2:41-46

LUKE 4:14-16

Where did the early church worship?
ACTS 2:46

ACTS 16:13-15

ROMANS 16:3-5

IS A CHURCH BUILDING IMPORTANT FOR WORSHIP?
God does not make his presence known to believers in a special building in special ways as he did in the Temple. The coming of Jesus has changed all that. When Jesus died, the Temple curtain (which was as thick as a carpet) split in two. Jesus' death had brought God and sinners together. (This is called the atonement.)

What is worship?

3 (continued) Worship of God in Old Testament times was different from worship in New Testament times.

God makes his presence known to Christians through the Holy Spirit. The building a church meets in is just a convenient place for Christians to get together in one place. What kinds of places do Christians use for worship in your town?

4 The Bible tells us how God wants to be worshipped.

Read the following verses and find out more:

ISAIAH 29:13

1 CORINTHIANS 11:17-18

1 CORINTHIANS 14:40

HEBREWS 12:28-29

COLOSSIANS 3:16

EPHESIANS 5:19-20

What is worship?

5 How did the early church worship?

Read the following verses to find out more:

ACTS 1:14

ACTS 20:7

1 CORINTHIANS 16: 1-2

COLOSSIANS 3:16-17

2 TIMOTHY 4:2

6 How does your church worship?

Look at the copy of your church bulletin or order of service and find out.

Help—it's sermon time!

1 What is a sermon?

The sermon is an important part of a worship service. What is a sermon? Write down your ideas.

2 I find sermons:

a) hard to understand ☐Yes ☐No
b) long ☐Yes ☐No
c) boring ☐Yes ☐No
d) interesting ☐Yes ☐No
e) surprising ☐Yes ☐No
f) personal ☐Yes ☐No

3 WDJD? What did Jesus do?

When Jesus lived on earth he worshipped God and was sometimes asked to explain God's Word.
Read *LUKE 4:14-22*. What did Jesus do and say?

Preaching or teaching is another way of saying 'explaining God's Word'.
Read *ACTS 2:14-40*-here is an example of a sermon.
Can you list six important things you notice about Peter's sermon?

1.

2.

3.

4.

5.

6.

Help—it's sermon time!

4 Making the most of a sermon

Make a list of ideas to help someone who is about your age to listen to a sermon.

5 Practical tips

1. Pray for the preacher.
Why is this important?

2. Pray that the Lord will speak to you.
Why is this important?

3. Make sure you have your Bible with you.
Why is this important?

4. Take a notebook.
Why is this important?

5. Make sure you write down the following things:
- Date
- Preacher's name
- Main Bible passage
- Sermon title
- A note of the Bible verses mentioned in the sermon

Help—it's sermon time!

- The main points of the sermon
(Some preachers give headings, which is helpful.)
- Any points the preacher gives that make the sermon subject relevant to you
- Any questions you may have
- A note of anything you didn't understand

6. Make sure that you ask yourself this question:
'What can I do about what I have heard?'

7. Pray about what you have learned.

8. Put into practice what you have learned.

6 Homework

If you really want the Word of God to make a difference to your life, then it is a good idea to spend some time during the week thinking about the sermon as well as reading the Bible for yourself.
Some people have found this SPECS helpful in doing this.

Sins — Does the sermon passage tell me about anything in my life that does not please the Lord?

Promises — Is there a promise in the passage?

Examples — Are there good examples in the sermon passage for me to follow?

Commands — Is there a command for me to obey?

Stoppers — Is there a warning about anything that will stop me from following Jesus?

Sermon Notes Sheet-see next page

Help—it's sermon time!

6 (continued) Sermon notes sheet

Date:
Preacher:
Bible passage:
Sermon title:
Main points:

Questions to ask:

Things to think about:

One thing to remember:

Why do we baptize people?

In your church, you may baptize believers by immersion. In this section, we are going to find out what this means.

1 Last instructions

Read **MATTHEW 28:16-20**.
What were Jesus' last instructions to his disciples?

[ ]

2 What is 'baptism'?

Our word "baptize' is made up from a New Testament Greek word which means 'immerse'. It literally means to drench, to drown, to submerge.

In the time of the early church, people were often baptized very quickly after they confessed Jesus as Saviour and Lord.
Read **ACTS 8:34-39**.
Why was the man baptized?

[ ]

Read **ACTS 16:25-34**.
Why were the people in the jailer's family baptized?

[ ]

Read **ROMANS 6:4**.
Baptism is a symbol or picture of what has happened when someone becomes a Christian.
When you go down under the water, it is like

[ ]

When you come up from under the water, it is like

[ ]

Baptism does not make someone a Christian; it shows that he or she already is one.

Why do we baptize people?

3 Should all Christians be baptized?

What do you think? ☐Yes ☐No

What does the Bible teach?
MATTHEW 3:13-15

JOHN 3:22-23

MATTHEW 28:19

4 What does your church do?

Find out when your church baptizes Christians, where it takes place and what happens.

What happens at communion?

Some churches call it 'The Lord's Supper'

1 When did it start?

On the night before he was arrested, Jesus celebrated a special supper with his disciples-the Jewish Passover. This was a meal that the Jews celebrated to help them remember that God had freed them from slavery in Egypt and also from death. The blood of a lamb kept them safe.

That night Jesus told them that there was something he wanted them to do as a way of remembering him and his death. It was a way of them remembering what he was going to do for them.

Communion is like a memorial. What is a memorial for?

Why do Christians need a memorial to help them remember the death of Jesus? Read **LUKE 22:19**.

2 What is it for?

It is important to remember that what happens at communion is symbolic. That means that it represents or stands for something. Read **LUKE 22:17-20** and **1 CORINTHIANS 11:23-29**.

Why is communion held regularly by Christians?
Read **LUKE 22:19**

1 CORINTHIANS 10:16-17

What happens at communion?

2 (continued) What is it for?

1 CORINTHIANS 11:26

What is important in a communion service?
Read **LUKE 22:17-19**.

What is the meaning of the communion service?
LUKE 22:19-20

What does the wine represent?

What does the bread represent?

3 Who takes communion?

Read **1 CORINTHIANS 11:27-29**.

What happens at communion?

4 For how long should Christians carry on holding communion services?

Read *1 CORINTHIANS 11:26*

5 What is Jesus looking forward to?

Read *LUKE 22:16*.

Read *REVELATION 21:27*.

6 What does your church do?

See if you can find out when your church celebrates communion and what happens.

That strange word Fellowship

1 Sorting out the word

Have you seen the film 'The Lord of the Rings-The Fellowship of the Ring' or read the book by J R R Tolkien?

What was the 'fellowship'?

How did they share with one another?

2 Christian fellowship

'Fellowship' means something that is shared. This is something very special to Christians. Imagine going on holiday abroad and going to church on Sunday. The service is in a language you don't understand but you feel at home. People in the church make you very welcome and when they hear that you have come from a church in another country they want you to send greetings when you get home. It's almost as if these Christians were part of your family-and yet you don't speak their language and they only speak a little English. That feeling is because of the fellowship that Christians have with each other. Christians share a saving faith in Jesus and a love for him, and that is something that helps them to have a relationship with one another.

3 Three Bible pictures

Christian fellowship is about belonging. Belonging to a church, being a member, is very important to many Christians. Belonging is very important in a church. Read **EPHESIANS 2:19-21**.

What does the apostle Paul say about belonging? He uses three pictures to help us understand this.

1

2

3

That strange word Fellowship

4 What does it mean?

Fill in the table.

Name	Rights	Responsibilities
A citizen of God's kingdom		
A family		
Stones in a building		

5 Christian fellowship is a practical thing

The first Christians shared fellowship in practical ways. Read the following verses to find out what they did:

ACTS 2:44-46

ROMANS 15:26

GALATIANS 6:6

PHILIPPIANS 4:14-19

6 What does your church do?

Look at the church bulletin or order of service and talk to a church member. See if you can make a list of the many ways your church shares fellowship.

Am I really a Christian? How can I be sure?

This is one of the most common questions asked by young people, especially those who have grown up in a Christian family or have been coming to church, Sunday School or young people's meetings for a long time.

Some people think that if they can't remember the exact day that they became Christians, then it means that they are not. This is not so.

If someone is truly a Christian it means that certain things have happened in that person's life. Look up these verses to find out:

ACTS 2:38

ACTS 16:30-31

2 CORINTHIANS 5:17

If a person becomes a Christian, then he or she wants to be sure. That is understandable; after all it is an important thing. It is a matter of life and death! The Bible calls the state of being sure that you are saved ASSURANCE: and this is something that God wants every true Christian to have.

Am I really a Christian? How can I be sure?

Read **HEBREWS 10:22**

ROMANS 8:38-39

1 Doubts about being a Christian

It is not unusual to doubt whether or not you really have been saved from your sins. Ask an older Christian! But doubts can be unhelpful. Imagine if you planted a sunflower seed in your garden. You are worried that it is not growing and so every morning you go into the garden and dig up the seed to see how much it has sprouted and how long the roots are. What will happen to that plant? Well, it might not survive all the digging up, and even if it does, it won't be a strong plant! So it is with doubting Christians. They will never be strong Christians.

2 Becoming a Christian

What does the Bible teach us about becoming a Christian?
Read **JOHN 3:3**

1 TIMOTHY 1:15

EPHESIANS 2:8-9

Am I really a Christian? How can I be sure?

3 Changes

Ask yourself these questions:

- ☐ Do I believe that I am a sinner?
- ☐ Do I believe that Jesus died to save sinners?
- ☐ Have I repented of my sin?
- ☐ Am I putting my whole faith and trust only in Jesus Christ to save me from my sin?
- ☐ Am I seeing evidence of change in my life?
- ☐ If so, what?
- ☐ Is the Holy Spirit working in my life?

The Holy Spirit is God's gift to every believer the moment that person trusts Jesus for salvation. The Holy Spirit lives in Christians giving them power to live for God. Read **ROMANS 5:5**

What changes do you notice in the lives of these people when they became Christians?
Zacchaeus—**LUKE 19:8-10**
Paul—**ACTS 7:58; ACTS 9:1-4; ACTS 9:19-22**

4 Look to God

If you want to be sure that you are a Christian, then ask God to give you assurance. He really does want you to know whether you are a Christian or not. Read **1 JOHN 5:13**

How will God answer your prayer for assurance?

- He will answer in the same way that he answers all our other prayers.

- Through the reading and preaching of his Word, the Bible.

- Through the advice of older, mature Christians.

- Through giving us the peace which passes all understanding.

- Through our being able to see changes in our lives that we can only explain by the fact that it is God at work.

Becoming a Christian-what then?

1 Growing is important

Imagine you had a baby brother or sister. What would you think if the baby was the same size at ten months old as he/she had been at ten weeks old? What would happen?

When we become Christians, God does not intend for us to stay 'baby Christians'; he wants us to grow.
Read *2 PETER 3:18*.

2 Growing Christians

Read *ACTS 2:37-47*.
On the Day of Pentecost about three thousand people became Christians and they began to grow in their faith. What was it that helped them to grow?

- Listening to God's Word
- Fellowship with other Christians
- Remembering Jesus' death in the breaking of bread-we call this communion
- Prayer
- Helping one another
- Meeting together to worship and praise God

How do you think these things helped them to grow in their faith?

Becoming a Christian-what then?

How do you think these things will help you to grow as a Christian?

3 More about growing

Read these verses and see if you can find more help:
JOSHUA 1:8

HEBREWS 5:12-14

HEBREWS 10:24-25

4 An old poem: 'If Jesus came to your house'

This is a very old poem. We are not sure who wrote it, but it seems to have been written to make Christians think about how they are living and growing. Growing as a Christian is not just about growing in knowing about Jesus, but also growing to be more like Jesus. We call this holiness. People don't talk much about this today but it is just as important to the Lord as it ever was!

Let's hope the author of the poem wouldn't mind a few alterations to bring it more up to date!

Becoming a Christian-what then?

4 (continued) An old poem: 'If Jesus came to your house'

If Jesus came to your house to spend a day or two,
If he came unexpectedly, I wonder what you'd do?
Oh, I know you'd give your best room to such an honoured guest,
And the food that you would serve him would be your very best.
And you would keep assuring him you're glad to have him there,
That having him in your own home was joy beyond compare!

But when you saw him coming, would you meet him at the door
With outstretched arms to welcome your heavenly visitor?
Or would you have to change your clothes, before you let him in?
Or hide some DVDs and put the Bible where they'd been?
Would you turn off your CD player and hope he hadn't heard
And wish you hadn't shouted that last, loud, angry word?
Would you hide your gameboys, computer games and books?
Could you let Jesus walk right in and take a careful look?

And I wonder, if the Saviour spent a day or two with you,
Would you go on doing the things you always do?
Would you go right on saying the things you always say?
Would life go on just as it has from day to day?
Would you watch TV and read the books you usually read?
And let him know the things on which your mind and spirit feed?

Would you take Jesus with you where you'd planned to go,
Or maybe, would you change your plans, for just a day or so?
Would you be glad to have him meet your very closest friends,
Or hope that they would stay away, until his visit ends?

Would you be glad to have him stay, for ever, on and on?
Or would you sigh with great relief when he, at last, was gone?
It would be very interesting to know the things that you would do
If Jesus came in person to spend some time with you.

(Altered, Anonymous)

Becoming a Christian-what then?

5 Help with Bible reading

Reading God's word, the Bible, is essential (absolutely necessary) for Christian growth.

However, the Bible isn't always an easy book to understand. Don't worry, there is plenty of help available.

Ask your youth leader or Sunday School teacher about ordering some Bible study notes especially written to help children and young people to understand the Bible.

If you have a young people's library in your church, you may well find some helpful books there. There are many exciting true stories about Christians who have had adventures following Jesus!

Let's review
Morning service help-sheet

Date:

Leader of service:

Preacher:

How would you describe the first hymn?
(e.g. Was it a song of praise, or something else?)

What was the children's talk about? (If there was one.)

What was the Bible reading?

Was the Bible reading the same passage as the passage for the sermon?
If not, what was the connection between the Bible reading and the sermon?

Who/what was prayed for?

Let's review
Morning service help-sheet

What was the theme of the hymn/song before the sermon?

What was the main subject of the sermon?

Write down the main points of the sermon, and any scripture references.

Was there anything you found difficult in the sermon?

How was the last hymn/song linked to the sermon?

Why do we sing hymns/psalms/songs?

Let's review
Morning service help-sheet

What subjects do we sing about?

What do you find easy/difficult to understand about the hymns/psalms/songs we sing?

How does the children's talk fit in with the rest of the service?

What kind of subjects are usually prayed for in the morning service?

Have the prayers ever helped you?

What are the sermons about at the moment?

Can you think of a sermon that has helped you?

Do you take notes during the sermon?

Let's review
Morning service help-sheet

If you have sermon notes given out in your church, do you use them?

What are you finding difficult about listening to sermons?

Do you have any questions?

Also available...

Sermon Notes

Sermon Notes Black
ISBN 978 1 84625 332 4
Page count 96

Sermon Notes Stripy
ISBN 978 1 84625 341 6
Page count 96

A useful tool for people who desire to enjoy sermons in a more constructive and useful manner.

This notebook gives space for making your sermon notes, with specific emphasise on points to look out for, as well as some popular Bible passages at the front.

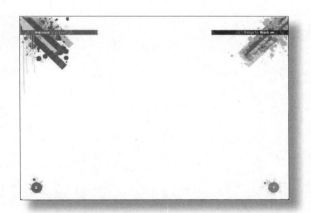

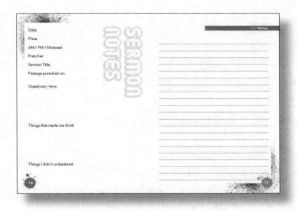

Published by Day One Publications
Ryelands Road, Leominster, HR6 8NZ
UK 01568 613 740 FAX 01568 611 473
USA 888-329-6630
email sales@dayone.co.uk
web site-www.dayone.co.uk
North American e-mail sales@dayonebookstore.com

North American web site www.dayonebookstore.com

DayOne

ISBN 978-1846253898

£3